My mom put up a big whiteboard.

She put it on the wall in the hall.

"This is for you to write notes on," said Mom.

"Then I will know what you need."

I liked this plan.

I picked up the pen and wrote my mom a note.

It said:

Dear Mom,

I need some math cards.

I need new boots.

Love,

Jade

Every day I thought of other things to add to the note.
By the end of the week, my note said:

Dear Mom,

I need some math cards, a toy boat, and a pet rat.

I need new boots, a red coat, and a pet rat.

I need a big ball, a red pen, and a pet rat.

We can go to the mall and get all these things.

       Love,

          Jade

Mom saw the note.

"Jade," she called. "This note is too long."

She took the pen and crossed out some things.

All she left were the math cards, the boots,

and the red pen.

Then we went to the mall to shop.

Most of the things we got fit into a small brown bag.
But one little thing Mom got, I put in my pocket!